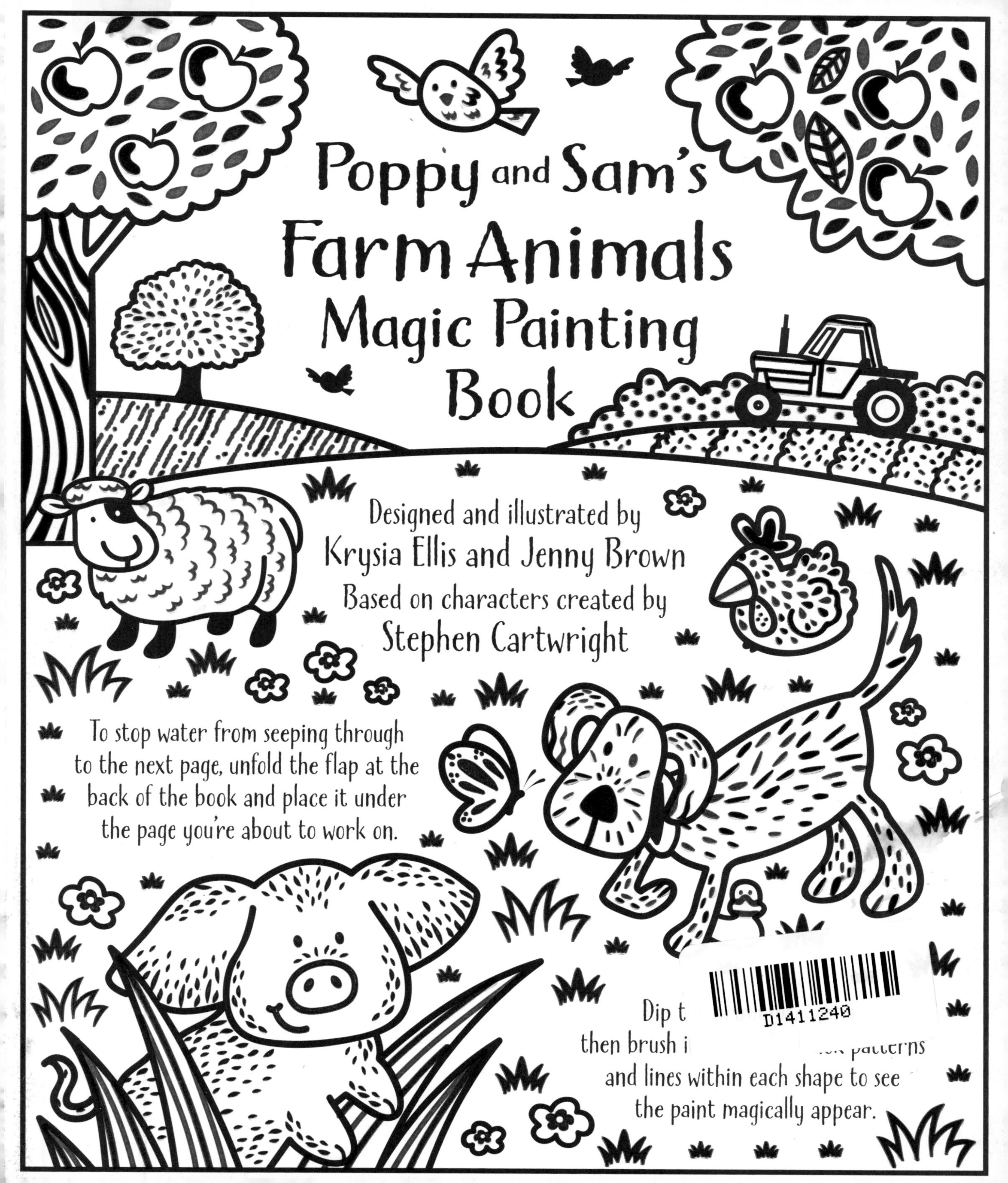
Poppy and Sam's
Farm Animals
Magic Painting
Book
Designed and illustrated by
Krysia Ellis and Jenny Brown
Based on characters created by
Stephen Cartwright
To stop water from seeping through
to the next page, unfold the flap at the
back of the book and place it under
the page you're about to work on.
Dip t
then brush i
patterns
and lines within each shape to see
the paint magically appear.
D1411240

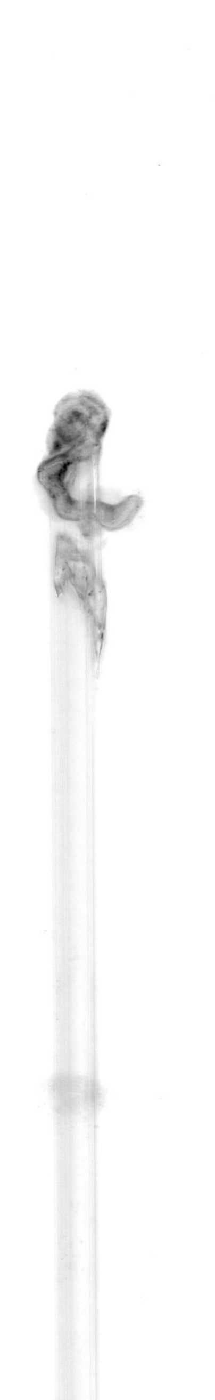